THE RAF QUIZ BOOK

EUNICE WILSON

GRUB STREET · LONDON

Published by Grub Street, The Basement, 10 Chivalry Road, London SW11 1HT

Copyright © Grub Street 1993
Text Copyright © Eunice Wilson 1993

A catalogue for this title is available from the British Library

ISBN 0 948817 69 0

Aircraft drawings by David Marchant RNAS
Most photographs are reproduced from the archive of
247 (F) China British Squadron Association

Additional photographs courtesy Norman Franks

Typeset by BMD Graphics, Hemel Hempstead

Printed and bound by Biddles Ltd, Guildford and King's Lynn

ACKNOWLEDGEMENTS

With many thanks to the members of the 247 (F) Squadron
Association, who have answered many questions over the years,
general and particular, and whose help has enabled these
questions to come together in a book.

Special thanks to Wg Cdr W E Browne, Sqn Ldr Phil Murton, Flt Lt Ian Pride
and Norman Franks for checking the draft copy.

The book is dedicated to 247 (F) The China British Squadron

HOW MUCH DO YOU KNOW ABOUT THE ROYAL AIR FORCE?

Well, here's your chance to find out, by trying to answer the 400 questions in this book and keeping your score as you go.

If you are an RAF buff, more than likely many answers will already be in your memory. If not, or if you can't quite remember them, though it's on the tip of your tongue, you'll be able to find most of the answers in some form or other in the many books now available in aviation bookshops or your local library.

I hope this book might lead you on to discovering more information, or even making up your own quiz. Or why not send your questions and answers to me, Eunice Wilson, they'll be more than welcome, and the best will be included in the next edition.

You may even be considering a career in the Royal Air Force where there are equal opportunities for men and women in all ranks and skills; if this is to be your future, best of luck.

1   On what date was the RAF formed and from what?

2   What did 2nd TAF in 1944 stand for?

3   This was the only biplane to fly in the Battle of Britain. What is it?

4   Who was Fighter Command's only VC?

5   What was the dual rank held by RFC officers?

6   Where is Condover?

7   What was its wartime function?

8   Where is the Battle of Britain Memorial Flight based?

9   What is the home station of the Red Arrows?

10   What is the oldest squadron in the RAF?

11   What is Tangmere famous for?

12   What was the name of the Lancaster bomber's predecessor?

13   Where was No 1 Parachute Training School, and what is it now?

14 What part did Carlisle airport play in WW2?

15 No 10 Group was responsible for which part of the country? Where was its HQ and what was it called? What is it now?

16 What is an EFTS?

17 Who makes the Harrier VTOL aircraft?

18 Where is the Bader Arms in Sussex?

19 What is a two and a halfer?

20 What rank do these sleeve stripes indicate?

Now add up your score and enter here _____

1   Where is the RAF College?

2   Who was the RFC pilot who shot down the first Zeppelin over the UK in WW1?

3   What was Leefe Robinson awarded?

4   Which were the first bomber aircraft?

5   When was the first German daylight bombing raid on London in WW1?

6   Where can you check the facts in this book from the original documents?

7   How many Commands were there in WW2?

8   What is the number of the form on which daily operational records were and still are written?

9   Can you identify this helicopter and can you name a station where it is currently in operation?

10   What do two horizontal chevron stripes on the upper sleeve signify?

11   What does a winchman do?

12 What do the letters RCAF, RNZAF, and RAAF stand for?

13 What was the name of the engine in the first Spitfire?

14 For what purpose were the black and white stripes painted on the wings and fuselage of fighter aircraft in WW2, as shown in this old photograph?

15 What were Q sites?

16 When was the Fleet Air Arm formed?

17 Where is the RAF Museum?

18 What was a double winged aircraft called?

19 What was the 1943 co-operation between Havocs and Hurricanes called? What did they do?

20 Where are RAF personnel records held?

Now add up your score and enter here _____

1   There was only one general Muster Roll made of the RAF and that was in number order. When was it made and where can it be seen now?

2   What is the popular name for non-jet aircraft? And how can you tell the difference by 'just looking'?

3   Why are rescue aircraft painted yellow or day-glo orange?

4   What colour were the aircraft used by the RAF in WW2 for air photo reconnaissance? Why?

5   There were two famous fighter pilots with two artificial legs? Who were they?

6   This is the lowest commissioned rank in the RAF, what is it and what is its equivalent in the army?

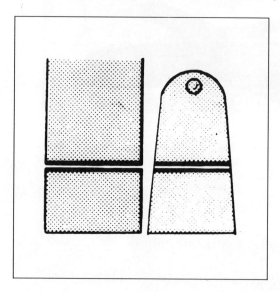

7   What was the name of the best known Irish fighter ace of WW2? Where was he born and what is his Memorial?

8   What do the letters ATA stand for? What did they do? What was unusual about them?

9 What is the difference between a helicopter and a fixed wing aircraft?

10 Which was Britain's No 1 RAF station?

11 Who was Igor Sikorsky?

12 Who invented the jet engine?

13 When were they first seriously used?

14 What is this aircraft and what is unusual about it?

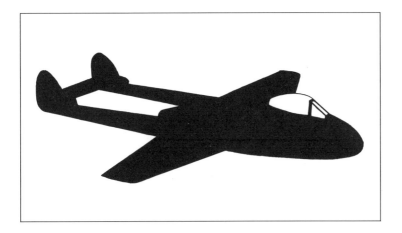

15 Who was English Electric's test pilot on Vampires?

16 What are the official dates of the Battle of Britain?

17 When is Battle of Britain Day?

18 What is Wings Week for?

19 Where is the RAF Memorial to those of no known grave?

20 Which and where is the RAF's own church?

Now add up your score and enter here _____

1   Where is Bomber Command's Roll of Honour kept? Why?

2   Who was the leader of the Dambusters?

3   Where in England did they practice?

4   What was the number of their squadron?

5   When did Ansons retire from service with the RAF?

6   Who led the first RAF jet crossing of the Atlantic?
    And when?

7   Which was the first Vampire Wing after WW2?

8   This was the peacetime marking of which Squadron (black
    and white chequerboard) and what was their nickname?

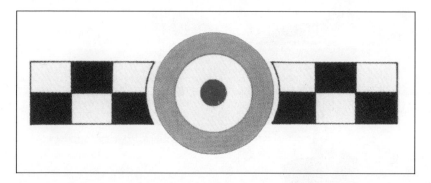

9   Who designed the Spitfire? When were they first delivered
    to the RAF?

10 Which aircraft and which squadrons operated from a frozen
    lake in Norway in 1940?

11 What were Faith, Hope and Charity? Where were they?

12 What were navigators called originally?

13 What is a gong?

14 What does SOE stand for?

15 This aircraft was flown by the Dambusters, what is it?

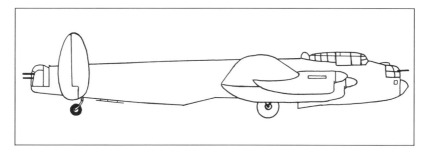

16 What is the usual colour of writing paper for letters from RAF squadrons and units?

17 This was the main aircraft used for landing agents into the occupied Continent, by the SOE from Tangmere, what is it?

18 Bloodhound missiles were first deployed in the UK in July 1958. Where were they based and by which command were they operated?

19 Which missiles were used in the Falklands by the UK forces, and against what?

20 What was 93 Squadron's motto?

Now add up your score and enter here _____

1   What was a Stalag Luft?

2   At which camp was the notorious incident of the murder of 50 RAF officers?

3   Where is the Polish Air Force Memorial?

4   Name six Free French Air Force Squadrons with the RAF in WW2.

5   What were the RAF Squadrons called which were manned by USA volunteers?

6   Who was the first American pilot shot down and killed with the RAF in the Battle of Britain?

7   Identify this aircraft and name one of its primary functions.

8   When was Bomber Command formed?

9   Who was Bomber Command's Commanding Officer in Chief, at its beginning?

10 Who was the Air Officer Commanding Fighter Command at its birth?

11   Who was the creator of the Hurricane?

12   What was the original name of RAF Uxbridge?

13   What is a cadre squadron?

14   By what name was Lawrence of Arabia known when in the RAF? Where was he stationed in 1922? What is the title of his book which describes this place?

15   What was Croydon airport known as originally?

16   What nickname were these inflatable life jackets known by and why?

17   Who was the youngest VC of WW2?

18   What does ATC mean?

19   Who designed the 'bouncing bomb'?

20   Which squadron carried them to the Möhne Dam?

Now add up your score and enter here _____

1   The American P38 fighter was known by another name with
    the RAF. What was it and what other British fighter took the
    same name in the mid-1950s?

2   Where is the School of Technical Training?

3   Across the road from what was once RAF Atcham, near
    Shrewsbury, are the remains of an important Roman
    encampment. What is its name and what is the coincidence
    which links the soldiers there to the American airmen at
    Atcham?

4   Where is the HQ of RAF Support Command?

5   Who landed at Tern Hill in 1906? What in?

6   What rank is P/O?

7   At which RAF station was the Paddington-Birkenhead
    express stopped so that airmen could get back to their base
    after a night out?

8   What is an erk?

9   What does the RAF's motto Per Ardua Ad Astra mean?

10 When Ollerton was re-named in 1942 by the Navy, what was its new name?

11 Who built the now disused airfield at High Ercall?

12 How fast is a knot?

13 What is a SACW?

14 Where is the RAF's Aerospace Museum?

15 In receiving an award would the non-commissioned ranks receive a cross or a medal?

16 What is drag?

17 What is a BAe 125?

18 By what name were perimeter tracks first known?

19 What occupation does this collar badge signify?

20 33 SLG (Satellite Landing Ground) at Weston Park in Shropshire, was on the estate of a stately home. Which, and where is it?

Now add up your score and enter here _____

1 What was MacRoberts Reply? Which aircraft bears the name now?

2 Who are 'The Saints'?

3 Which RAF Squadron originated the 'shark mouth'?

4 What is RAF Germany's principal role?

5 Which was the first American Eagle Squadron of the RAF?

6 What were Ramrods, Roadsteads, No-balls?

7 Can you name this aircraft and what was the reason for its decline in production?

8 19 June 1952, Crown Princess Astrid of Norway unveiled a stone monolith Memorial. To whom and where?

9 Who were the Black Arrows?

10 What was Der Adler Tag? And what was its date?

11 For what did RAF Tilstock use Bridleway Gate?

12 Where is the Douglas Bader public house?

13 What was a Hamilton Fort? Where might one be seen preserved?

14 Where is Sqn Ldr Caesar Hull DFC buried? In which squadron was he killed?

15 Bentley Priory at Stanmore in Middlesex, was designed by which architect? When? It is the HQ of which Command?

16 Who was the top scoring Czech fighter pilot in the RAF in WW2?

17 Who was the one-armed Commanding Officer of No 1 Squadron in 1941?

18 Who set the World Speed record for the second time from Tangmere in 1953? And what speed did he achieve?

19 What are the ranks of the ground staff at front right and second from the right at the back in this old photograph?

20 What special privilege did Auxiliary Air Force personnel enjoy at the beginning of the war?

Now add up your score and enter here _____

1 This was the RAF's first jet fighter, what is it and when was its first flight?

2 Which squadron was the first to receive jet aircraft delivery and when?

3 What was Germany's first jet fighter aircraft?

4 Who first caused a flying bomb to dive into the ground by catching its wing with his wing tip?

5 When did jet aircraft join 2nd TAF operationally?

6 Who was the highest ranking officer fighter pilot to be killed in the Battle of Britain?

7 What does 'in the drink' mean?

8 What does 7/10ths cloud mean?

9 When did the Hurricane IIc come into service? What was their advantage?

10 What is a vector?

11 Why did biplanes disappear?

12 What does STOL mean?

13 What are circuits and bumps?

14 What does 'ab initio' mean?

15 Sometimes you will see a WW2 pilot with a small golden eagle on his left pocket under his wings. What is the significance?

16 What does u/t mean?

17 What is a wind sock? Where will you see one?

18 What were the following in WW2, B58; B78; B86; B112?

19 What did these numbers represent?

20 This was South Africa's first air ace of WW2, who was he?

Now add up your score and enter here _____

1 Of the letters and numbers on the side of an aircraft's fuselage, which ones do not change unless for exceptional reasons?

2 What is the motto of 280 ASR Squadron?

3 And of 617 Squadron?

4 What was a Wimpy?

5 What is this aircraft and which was the first RAF squadron to receive it?

6 Where can you see the original RAF operational record books?

7 What was the original name for single wing aircraft?

8 Which aircraft can carry Tiger Cat short-range surface-to-air guided missiles?

9 What is the Morse Code for SOS?

10 Where was Concorde built and by whom?

11   How was RAF Brockton disguised?

12   To which now disused airfield did the first American Pursuit
     Group come in 1942?

13   What does RAFG mean?

14   What is the RAFA?

15   What type of aircraft flew in the Schneider Trophy contests?

16   What does Mark mean?

17   What is this aircraft and who produced it?

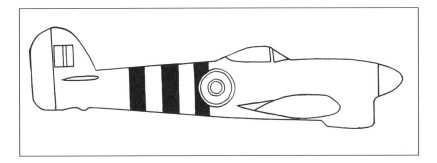

18   What is Westland's dominant post-war production?

19   Where was Hawker's design and development unit
     during WW2?

20   What did ASR stand for during the last war?

Now add up your score and enter here _____

1   What is the slang for gold braid on the peak of a uniform hat?

2   Which is the first rank to have gold braid on the hat?

3   During WW2 what was the minimum age for RAF recruiting?

4   Which takes precedence over the other, the DFC or the DSO?

5   Of which squadron was Winston Churchill honorary Commanding Officer?

6   Here are three drawings of a Spitfire, from different angles. What are the technical terms for views A, B and C?

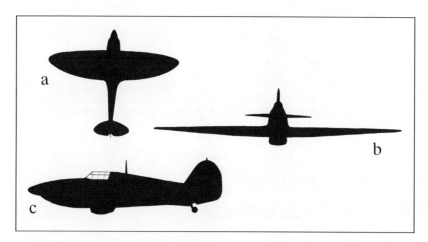

7   Which aircraft does 617, the Dambusters Squadron, now fly (1992)?

8   Where was 17 Squadron based in 1988?

9   What are the aircraft markings of No 17 Squadron, the Black Knights?

10 What relation was the wartime ace Denys Gillam to another star pilot, Harold Bird-Wilson, 'Birdy'?

11 What were women in the RAF known as in WW2?

12 A special type of flying training was undertaken at Chetwynd, near Newport. What was it?

13 Where is the RAF Staff College?

14 What does VSTOL mean?

15 What rank do these three chevrons and crown indicate?

16 Where will you find helicopter pilots under training?

17 What was a 'Grand Slam'?

18 What is the highest rank in the RAF?

19 What was the lowest in WW2?

20 No 1 Royal Canadian Air Force changed its number in 1941. To what?

Now add up your score and enter here _____

1 How many basic types of Tornado are there?

2 Who was Gubbins?

3 Where was RAF Bratton?

4 What was the word describing aircrew who were not captured when they landed in Germany or the occupied countries in WW2?

5 What was the ace 'Ginger' Lacey's first name?

6 Which aircraft have replaced Nimrods?

7 What is the nearest land base for aircraft on their way to the Falklands?

8 What nickname was used to describe wearers of this sleeve badge and what was their job?

9 What was an Intruder?

10 Where is the HQ of the RAF Provost Branch?

11 Which was the first RAF Eagle Squadron?

12 What was the Battle of Heaven?

13 What were the main tasks of Mosquitos?

14 Who built them?

15 What does PRU stand for?

16 What is this medal?

17 Which two aircraft were the main RAF combatants in the Battle of Britain?

18 What was the usual aircraft supplied for the use of COs of 1944 Communications Squadrons?

19 Which were the two main aircraft used by Air Sea Rescue?

20 What is the room or building called where RAF personnel eat and relax?

Now add up your score and enter here _____

1   Which aircrew member wore the O brevet?

2   How many were in the crew of a Mosquito?

3   What are UASs?

4   What was the significance of the unfastened top button of this pilot's tunic?

5   From which country did the word radar come?

6   What was Knickbein?

7   What are Penguins?

8   What is a prang?

9   What is AA?

10 What were these called?

11 What is the officer assistant to the CO called, who kept the records of the unit?

12 What does RNoAF mean?

13 Which was the 'Millionaires Squadron'?

14 Which squadron was called 'The City of Birmingham'?

15 Which squadron was called 'The Fellowship of the Bellows'?

16 What is the significance of the gold tasselled lanyard – augilettes and devices – round the right shoulder of an RAF Officer?

17 What was the original name of RAF Peplow?

18 What is RAF Lindholme now?

19 What do the letters NCO stand for?

20 What does the world 'posted' mean?

Now add up your score and enter here _____

1 Who was the manufacturer of Typhoons?

2 How many Commands are there now? What are they?

3 How many battle honours may be blazoned on a Standard?

4 Who built the RAF church of St Clement Dane's in the Strand, London.

5 There were severe cutbacks in the RAF when squadrons were disbanded or amalgamated. When was this?

6 What is a 'gift' squadron?

7 What is the significance of this goat?

8 For what is the Dacre Trophy awarded annually to a Strike Command Squadron?

9   What colour were aircraft painted for service in the Gulf?

10   What is the motto of No 1 Squadron?

11   Where is Luqa?

12   Where and when was No 8 Squadron formed?

13   How many rotors has a Chinook?

14   Which squadron flew VC 10s and carried the names of what and who?

15   In WW2, what was a 'circus'?

16   What is meant by 'low visibility markings'?

17   When did the RAF fly the last Lightning?

18   Where is Tengah airfield?

19   What does RAF Lyneham do?

20   What squadron does this livery designate, with its red X's?

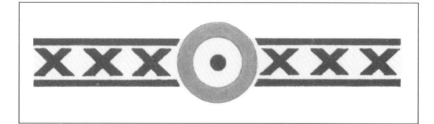

Now add up your score and enter here _____

1 With which city is No 43 Squadron associated?

2 Why was 247 Squadron called 'The China British'?

3 When No 1 Squadron shared Tangmere with 43, what did they nickname themselves?

4 How many crew does a Phantom carry?

5 And a Jaguar?

6 What was a 'Diver'?

7 What does SAM mean?

8 Which aircraft does No 15 Squadron currently (1992) fly?

9 Where was No 60 Squadron in 1967? Flying what?

10 What is this aircraft and who flies them?

11 How old must a squadron be before it is granted a Standard?

12 Who was the Red Baron?

13 How many 'kills' did a pilot have to have confirmed before he could be called an 'ace'?

14 In the main, during WW2, unit markings, other than code letters, were obliterated. Why?

15 What was a 'Blue Diamond'?

16 What were Black Lysanders?

17 What was 'Treble One'?

18 Which squadron is commemorated at Woodhall Spa? What shape does the Memorial take?

19 Where on a uniform would you expect to find this badge?

20 What were 'impressed' aircraft?

Now add up your score and enter here _____

1 What was the meaning of the codeword 'Corporate'?

2 What was an ACH (GD)?

3 What is a 'chopper'?

4 Which Group comprises today's Strike Command?

5 What was Operation Overlord?

6 What was the airlift to Berlin codenamed in 1948-9?

7 What type of cloud is this Spitfire flying through and why was it such a hazard to pilots?

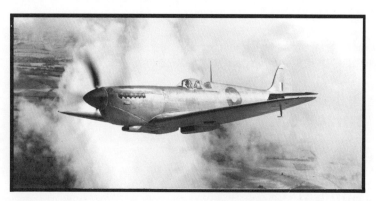

8 What was a Rhubarb?

9 A number of squadrons of the RAF were involved in the Battle of the Atlantic, name any three of them.

10 What are the RAF colours?

11 What was the RAF winged brooch called as given to the womenfolk of airmen of WW2?

12 Where is No 2 FTS? What does it fly?

13 How many gliding schools are there in the RAF?

14 What does CFS mean? And where are its units?

15 No 1 Photographic Unit in 1988 was where?

16 Which famous squadron is now home based at Marham?

17 What kind of aircraft does 10 Squadron fly at RAF Brize Norton?

18 What type of aircraft is shown here and what is mounted on the wing?

19 What is Skyflash?

20 Which aircraft first carried Harpoons?

Now add up your score and enter here _____

1 Who was Chief of Defence Staff in 1991?

2 Which are the nearest air force stations to London?

3 Where in northern England, in particular, did they complain about low level flying?

4 Where is RAF Wildenrath?

5 Who was the famous Wing Commander CO of 76 Squadron in 1943?

6 On what date did the Lancaster fly for the first time?

7 Where is the Airmen's Command School?

8 How can you tell just by looking at this picture exactly what the aircraft is and how could you find out more about its particular history?

9   Round which US – ex RAF – station did the peace Women gather?

10 What replaced the Observer's O?

11 Where were the RAF sequences in the film 'Perfect Hero' made?

12 What is the highest award RAF Catering sections can achieve?

13 Who was the Defence Secretary when the Gulf War began?

14 Where in 1944 might one have found an otter with wings?

15 What is the equivalent rank in the navy of a Squadron Leader?

16 What are the only three things a prisoner of war is allowed to disclose?

17 Although there is no international sign of surrender, what does a white flag signify?

18 In the phonetic alphabet as used in the Services in WW2, what words were used to signify F? And S? and U?

19 What is the name given to the rings on this aircraft's fuselage and what colours are they?

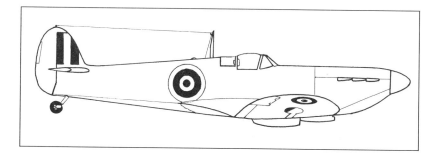

20 What are its wartime colours on camouflage?

Now add up your score and enter here _____

1   From what language does the distress call May Day come? And what does it mean?

2   For what do the following letters stand? LG; ALG; i/c; OR; SASO; RAFO; W.e.f; r/g?

3   Which is the port side?

4   What is an echelon?

5   What is a fix?

6   What does fore and aft mean?

7   What units does a Group consist of?

8   Match these sleeve rings to their correct ranks.

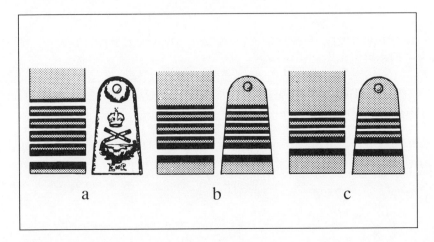

a   b   c

9   What is drift?

10   What is the nickname of 74 Squadron?

11   Where were Irvin parachutes made?

12   Who made the Sword of Peace?

13 On what type of aircraft did the Duchess of York qualify as a pilot?

14 Which were the last stations in 1991 to have Bloodhound missiles?

15 What are MEDAs?

16 Which RAF station during 1990-1 became very famous for its VIP treatment of returning hostages?

17 What can VTOL aircraft do that other fixed wings cannot?

18 Who led the first Meteor jet squadron from Colerne to Molesworth in 1945?

19 Which aircraft delivers the bulk of emergency supplies to famine stricken countries?

20 Where would you see these stars on a blue background and which rank do they signify?

Now add up your score and enter here _____

1   Where was the International Air Tattoo held for the RAF Benevolent Fund?

2   Where is RAF Akrotiri?

3   What is this famous decoration?

4   When was the first Battle of Britain Spitfire shot down?

5   What was the navy's version of the Spitfire?

6   Why was the special modification XXX used as a variation on the Spitfire's design?

7   What was 'pecking'?

8   Where does the statue of Bomber Harris stand?

9   Who was the sculptor?

10 Which gate-guardian stands outside RAF Innsworth near Gloucester?

11 For what does CARG stand?

12 What is the Cornwall Aircraft Park at Helston called?

13 This aircraft is nicknamed 'Fat Albert' and 'Herkybirds'. What is it?

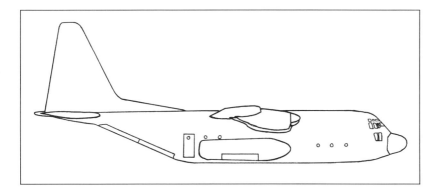

14 Where did King George VI learn to fly?

15 What type of aircraft is the bomber brought up from Loch Ness?

16 Which manufacturer built the Vulcan?

17 What type of aircraft was the Memphis Belle?

18 Who were the Poachers?

19 What was the base from which the Dambusters flew?

20 What symbol of his calling does an RAF Chaplain wear on his uniform?

Now add up your score and enter here _____

1 This famous NCO pilot was the only man ever to receive three DFMs. What is his name?

2 What was the meaning of the codename 'Flash'?

3 What did the codename 'Jubilee' stand for?

4 In which year was Operation 'Starkey'?
What was it meant to do?

5 Where was the 'Torch' invasion?

6 What does BAOR stand for? Was the RAF a part?

7 Which type of Russian aircraft was used to take allied equipment to the Gulf in 1990?

8 Which aircraft of WW2 was the first to have 'clipped' wings?

9 Which were the main UK air bases from where troops and equipment were flown to the Gulf?

10　By what codename was the Gulf known?

11　Who was the first British pilot to bale out of a plane in an emergency with a parachute? When?

12　Who produced the first British manually operated parachute?

13　GQ Ltd made ejector seats. Who was the first to use one?

14　In which squadrons were the Woods-Scawen brothers in the Battle of Britain?

15　What were the names of the RAF bases in Saudi Arabia in 1990?

16　Strike Command, 1992, consists of which Groups?

17　Which squadrons were disbanded in 1992?

18　What is this aircraft and what did it become famous for?

19　From where in the UK was the second Tornado GR1 Force deployed to the Gulf?

20　From what type of aircraft are Tornados refuelled?

Now add up your score and enter here _____

1 What was the Olive Trail?

2 On what date did Argentina invade the Falklands?

3 What is the name of the airfield on Ascension Island?

4 When was 57 Squadron disbanded?

5 What is this aircraft and what is special about it?

6 Who was the author of *The Darling Buds of May*?

7 What is the nickname for the RAF ensign?

8 What does 7644 Flight RAFVR do?

9 What is a Buccaneer?

10 What was the main opponent of the Spitfire and Hurricane in the early years of WW2?

11 About how long does it take for a modern jet fighter to reach 35,000 ft?

12   What shape is an F-117a, the US Stealth?

13   For how long has the RAF used female loadmasters?

14   Since what date has the USAF employed female pilots?

15   Where were the early RAF aerobatic displays held?

16   Who wrote the *The Penguin in the Eyrie*, about Coastal Command?

17   He was top scoring pilot in the Desert and later a famous test pilot helping to develop the Hawker Hunter. Who is he?

18   Of what is Charles, Prince of Wales, Colonel-in-Chief?

19   What is the 'Plastic Air Force'?

20   Why are you being asked army questions about the Gulf in a book about the RAF?

What is your final total? _____

A What is this plane and what armament did it carry?

B It was called the 'Flying Pencil', name this WW2 German bomber.

C   This German fighter ace later became General of the
    Luftwaffe fighter force. Who was he?

D This famous night fighter pilot later helped test Britain's first
jet airliner, the Comet. Who was he and what was his
nickname?

E Designed as a bomber at the end of WW1, in 1919 it was the first aircraft flown across the Atlantic, what is it?

F This was the last operational four prop-engined aircraft used by the RAF, what is it?

G His nickname was 'Stuffy'. Who was he?

H   What is this aircraft?

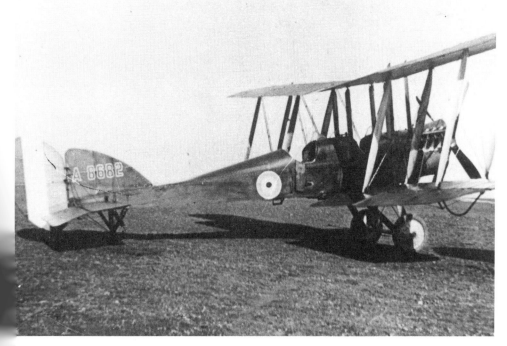

I   What is this plane and what was its function?

ANSWERS RAF QUIZ 1

1 1 April 1918, from an amalgamation of the RFC – Royal Flying Corps and the RNAS, Royal Naval Air Service.

2 Second Tactical Air Force, combined allied air forces for and after D-Day. Developed from Exercise Spartan, Z & Composite groups.

3 The Gloster Gladiator.

4 Wing Commander James B Nicholson VC.

5 They had an army as well as RFC rank, if seconded from an army unit.

6 3 miles south of Shrewsbury.

7 It was a Relief Landing Ground (RLG) in Shawbury.

8 RAF Coningsby.

9 RAF Scampton.

10 No 3, presently based at Gutersloh, Germany. Motto – The third shall be first.

11 A front-line Battle of Britain Airfield, peace-time home of 1 and 43 Squadrons, and now the Museum of Military Aviation.

12 The Avro Manchester.

13 At Ringway during WW2, now Manchester Airport.

14 Carlisle was an OTU, Operational Training Unit, which trained fighter pilots.

15 10 Group was responsible for the West Country and South Wales, it's HQ was and still is at Box in Wiltshire. Not now 10 Group but still called RAF Rudloe Manor.

16   Elementary Flying Training School.

17   British Aerospace.

18   In Tangmere village.

19   A Squadron Leader – one thin light blue stripe between two wider ones on each sleeve cuff.

20   The rank of Wing Commander.

ANSWERS RAF QUIZ 2

1   Cranwell, Lincolnshire.

2   Lt William Leefe Robinson, 2/3 Sept 1916 – shot down an SL11 Shütte Lanz.

3   The Victoria Cross.

4   Avro 504s bombed the Zeppelin sheds on their bases in Germany on 22 September 1914. Light bombers were the de Havilland DH4 and DH9; heavy bombers were the Handley Page 0/400.

5   28 Nov 1916, German LVG 1V bomber.

6   At the Public Record Office, Ruskin Avenue, Kew, Richmond, Surrey and at the RAF Museum, Hendon.

7   Nine. Balloon Command, Bomber, Coastal, Fighter, Maintenance, Overseas, Training, Ferry and Transport, Army Co-operation Commands.

8   F 540s – the diary, and F 541s – the flight records.

9   A Westland Wessex, flying from RAF Odiham.

10   A corporal.

11   Travels down the cable of a rescue helicopter to lift off the stranded or injured.

12   Royal Canadian Air Force, Royal New Zealand Air Force and Royal Australian Air Force.

13   A Merlin.

14   To indicate they were Allied aircraft, especially those part of the 2nd TAF (2nd Tactical Air Force), the invasion forces of 1944, which consisted of aircraft of different nationalities.

15   Mock airfields with fake buildings and aircraft set up some way from the real airfield to deceive the enemy.

16   1924.

17   Hendon in north London.

18   A biplane.

19   Turbinlite Squadrons. The Havocs carried a nose-mounted searchlight to light up bombers and aid the fighters to see the target at night.

20   Records of all ranks are at MOD RAF Innsworth, Gloucester.

ANSWERS RAF QUIZ 3

1   In 1918, at the creation of the RAF from the RFC. A copy is at the Public Record Office, Kew.

2   Piston engined. They have propellers, jets do not.

3   The yellows are the most visible colours at long distance on land, sea and in the air.

4   Light blue because they flew unarmed and very high and this colour is less easily seen against the sky.

5   Wing Commander Douglas Bader and F/O Colin Hodgkinson.

6   Pilot Officer and army equivalent is 2nd Lieutenant.

7   'Paddy' Brendan Finucane. Dublin. A block of flats in Richmond, Surrey.

8   Air Transport Auxiliary. They flew aircraft of all types, generally without crews, to and from factories to squadrons. Many of them were women, perhaps the most famous being Amy Johnson.

9   A helicopter has 'rotors' or revolving blades set above its fuselage so that it can rise vertically and hover.

10   Uxbridge.

11   A Russian born 1889 in St Petersburg, who designed and built the first helicopter.

12   A young RAF Flying Officer, Frank Whittle, later Sir Frank, first presented his original drawings of gas-turbined engines for jet propelled aircraft in 1928. With Dr A A Griffiths of the Royal Aircraft Establishment (RAe) at Farnborough, he produced the first jet engine which was tested there in 1937.

13   By Germany in 1943, built by the Heinkel Company. The first British jet aircraft was the Meteor flown in 1941 but not in service with the RAF until 1944.
     GLOSTER (E28/39) -- 15.5.41.

14 A Vampire. It has twin tail booms and appears to have two engines when it has only one.

15 Wing Commander Roland Beamont, 'Bee', who had flown Hurricanes in 87 Squadron in the Battle of Britain.

16 10 July to 31 October 1940.

17 15 September each year.

18 Used by the RAF Association to raise funds for RAF servicemen and their families.

19 On the Runnymede Memorial near Windsor.

20 St Clement Dane's church in the Strand, London.

ANSWERS RAF QUIZ 4

1 Lincoln Cathedral, because this was in the heart of 'bomber' country, the Cathedral was also a focal point for returning bombers.

2 Wg Cdr Guy Gibson.

3 Ladybower Reservoir near Sheffield.

4 617 Squadron.

5 28 June 1968.

6 Sqn Ldr R W Oxspring DFC in an English Electric/de Havilland Vampire, July 1948, for which he was awarded the AFC. He led six aircraft of 54 Squadron at Odiham, from UK to America, refuelling in Iceland.

7 Squadrons 247, 54 and 72 at Odiham formed the first Vampire Wing, in late 1946. Vampire F 1 built in Preston made its first maiden flight at Samlesbury 20 April 1945.

8 43 Squadron. The Fighting Cocks.

9 R J Mitchell. In June 1938, to 19 Squadron at Duxford, they were operational in August of same year.

10 Gladiators of 263 Squadron and Hurricanes of 46 Squadron.

11 Gladiators on Malta.

12 Observers.

13 A medal or decoration.

14 Special Operations Executive.

15 A Lancaster.

16 Pale Blue.

17 Black painted Westland Lysander.

18 The first surface-to-air missiles (SAM) were Bristol Ferranti's at RAF North Coates, Lincolnshire, controlled by Fighter Command.

19 Shrikes, against radar installations, carried by Vulcans. Harpoons went into Nimrod weapon bays but were not used in action.

20 Ad arma parati – ready for battle.

ANSWERS RAF QUIZ 5

1   A prisoner of war camp in Germany during WW2 for aircrew personnel.

2   Stalag Luft III at Sagan.

3   At Ruislip, beside RAF Northolt.

4   Any of the following squadrons: 326 to 329, 340, 341, 342, 345 to 347.

5   The RAF Eagle Squadrons.

6   Billy Fiske, killed 16 August 1940 at Tangmere, with 601 Squadron. He died in Chichester Hospital and is buried at Boxgrove Priory.

7   A de Havilland Tiger Moth, which was used extensively for early pilot training.

8   14 July 1936 located first at Uxbridge, but moved to Walters' Ash in the Chilterns, near High Wycombe, in 1939.

9   Air Chief Marshal Sir John Steel.

10   Air Marshal Sir Hugh Dowding.

11   Sydney Camm, knighted in 1953.

12   Hillingdon House, built in 1717 by the Duke of Schomberg as a hunting lodge. Early in the 1800s it was bought by Richard Henry Cox, heir to the banking firm of Cox and Kings, founded by his grandfather. In the Cox family until the death of Frederick it was offered for sale in 1913 and bought by the government in 1915. Originally it was going to be used as a camp for German prisoners of war.

13   A squadron formed partly of regular and partly of Special

Reserve personnel. Or the skeleton of a squadron, reduced to the minimum.

14 Aircraftman John Hulme Ross. At Uxbridge. *The Mint.*

15 Plough Lane, which ran between the two aerodromes Beddington and Waddon.

16 They were called a Mae West, named after the film star.

17 Sgt John Hannah.

18 Air Traffic Control or Air Training Corps.

19 Barnes Wallis.

20 617 Squadron, the Dambusters.

ANSWERS RAF QUIZ 6

1 Lightning, the P1 English Electric Lightning.

2 Halton, Buckinghamshire.

3 Uriconium was the camp of the 14th Legion of the Roman Army and RAF Atcham was the first UK home of the 14th USAAF Pursuit Group.

4 RAF Brampton in Huntingdon.

5 Major Atcherley force landed in a hot air balloon. He was the father of the famous RAF twin brothers.

6 Pilot Officer.

7 Rednal, which opened in 1942. Its satellite was Montford Bridge.

8   An aircraftman of the ground crew.

9   Through Endeavour to the Stars.

10 Hinstock.

11 Walker and Slater.

12 One nautical mile per hour (2,000 yds).

13 Senior Aircraftwoman.

14 Cosford.

15 A medal.

16 The air current released from the back of the aircraft and its wings in flight.

17 An executive jet built by British Aerospace.

18 Taxi ways.

19 Medical services.

20 Weston Park, on the A41, laid out by Capability Brown.

ANSWERS RAF QUIZ 7

1   A Stirling aircraft of XV Squadron, N6086, 1941, at Wyton, donated by Lady MacRobert to commemorate her three sons killed in WW2. Later she gave more and now aircraft 'F' of XV Squadron, (Tornados), who flew the original Stirling, carries the name.

2 No 16 Squadron, RAF Germany senior strike squadron (1991) where it has served since early 1958, then with Canberras.

3 No 16.

4 Offensive counter-air and long range interception, part of NATO defence.

5 71 Squadron with Buffaloes and Hurricane Is. 1940.

6 Ramrod – Often flown by several squadrons (later up to four Wings) of fighters against specific targets (mainly enemy occupied airfields) resulting in some of the biggest daylight air battles over France 1942-3.
Roadstead – anti-shipping strikes round enemy-occupied coasts, by rocket or bomb and cannon-armed Hurricanes and Typhoons.
No-ball – Codename for the V1, Flying Bomb or Doodle Bug sites. Attacks with rocket or bombs and cannon on launching ramps and surroundings, often well hidden, buildings, etc., which were difficult to find.

7 Hawker Hunter. This was the dominant aircraft in 1957, when there were severe cutbacks in the RAF and so its production was reduced.

8 At North Weald, to the Norwegians who flew and died whilst on this station and elsewhere in the UK. 331, 332, 333 were some of the squadrons so commemorated.

9 No 111 Squadron's aerobatic team, led in 1955, by Sqn Ldr Roger Topp with 22 all-black Hunters. The squadron was called Treble One.

10 Eagle Day. August 13, 1940. The biggest German attack in England on the RAF.

11 For parachute and container dropping in 1944.

12 At Martlesham Heath. Sir Douglas Bader opened it on
Friday 14 Sept 1979. He was stationed here, when leading
242 Squadron, Hurricane Mk IIa's.

13 The underground battle HQ at Stapleford Tawney in Essex.

14 St Andrew's churchyard, Tangmere. 43 Squadron.

15 1788, by Sir John Soane. Fighter Command.

16 Flt Lt Karel Kutelwascher DFC of No 1 Squadron 1942.
Nicknamed 'Kut'.

17 Sqn Ldr J A F MacLachlan who had lost an arm during a dog
fight over Malta in 1940.

18 Sqn Ldr Neville Duke, DSO, DFC, Hawker's chief test pilot.
Over the measured mile between Worthing and
Littlehampton at 727.63 mph on 7 Sept 1953.

19 A sergeant at front right and a corporal at the back.

20 They could not be posted away from their home base without
their personal permission. After mobilisation it caused
friction, so was rescinded.

ANSWERS RAF QUIZ 8

1 The Gloster Meteor 1. Flew on 5 March 1943.

2 Two Meteors were delivered to 616 Squadron on
12 July 1944.

3 The Messerschmitt – ME262 – began intercepting Allied
aircraft in June 1944. First victory in July 44.

4 F/Sgt George Tate in a Spitfire of 610 Sqn, 4 July 1944.

5   In January 1945, but there was no combat between the British and German jets.

6   Wg Cdr John Scatliff Dewar DSO, DFC, aged 33, of 87 Squadron. He was born in India in 1907.

7   To come down in the sea.

8   A sky little over half obscured by cloud.

9   1941. They were armed with cannon.

10 A straight directional finding guide line in space, given to a pilot by Control – the course of an aircraft in flight directed from the ground to its required position.

11 Their construction meant they were slower than monoplanes.

12 Short take off and landing.

13 Practice take offs, circuits and landings on the airfield by pilots in training, and regularly by those already experienced.

14 From the beginning of training.

15 Worn by Pathfinder Force Aircrew after they had completed the requisite number of sorties and proved themselves capable. The much coveted badge of this elite force – PFF – of Bomber Command.

16 Under training.

17 Directional tube of cloth flying from a mast to show the way the wind is blowing. On an airfield or wherever there is a need to know the wind direction.

18 Airfields of 2nd TAF (Second Tactical Air Force) in Europe after D-Day June 1944.

19 These are code numbers for 2nd TAF airfield in N. Europe.
B58 – Melsbroek, Belgium
B78 – Eindhoven, Holland
B86 – Helmond, Germany
B112 – Hopsten, Germany

20 Sqn. Ldr Adolf 'Sailor' Malan DSO, DFC of 74 Squadron.
So called because he had been in the merchant navy.

ANSWERS RAF QUIZ 9

1 The small black number and letter toward the tail of the fuselage. This is the aircraft's factory registration. They do not change no matter to which squadron or unit it is delivered. They MAY if the aircraft is completely refurbished for exhibition or private purposes, in which case its engine number is its identification. The letters either side of the roundel are its squadron and individual aircraft identification. These are changed according to its unit assignment.

2 'We shall be there'. An air sea rescue squadron.

3 Appropriately for the Dambusters – 'Apres moi, le deluge'. 'After me the Flood'.

4 RAF slang for a Wellington bomber named after the Popeye cartoon character – J Wellington Wimpy.

5 A Tornado. 27 Squadron first received it in May 1983 at Marham.

6 Public Record Office, but now mostly on microfilm, the originals having been moved for preservation to the military archive at Hayes.

7 Monoplane.

8   Hercules, Belfast or Wessex.

9    $\cdots\ ---\ \cdots$ Three dots, three dashes, three dots.

10   British Aerospace at Filton, Bristol.

11   Camouflaged netting hid hangars and buildings, which made them look like farm houses and barns. Real cattle grazed between painted hedges.

12   Atcham.

13   RAF Germany.

14   The RAF Association for serving and ex-members.

15   Racing sea-planes.

16   The upgraded development from Type 1 – e.g. Hurricane Mark IIc or Mk IIc.

17   A Typhoon. Hawker produced it.

18   Helicopters.

19   Claremont House, Esher.

20   Air Sea Rescue.

ANSWERS RAF QUIZ 10

1   Scrambled Egg.

2   Group Captain.

3   Seventeen and a quarter years.

4 DSO – Distinguished Service Order followed by Distinguished Flying Cross.

5 615 County of Surrey Auxiliary Air Force, 'Churchill's Own'.

6 A is plan view, B is head on and C is profile.

7 Panavia Tornados, based at Marham in Norfolk.

8 RAF Bruggen, Germany.

9 A red gauntlet on a black/white shield and a white arrowhead pointing forward with black zig zags.

10 Brother-in-law; Gillam's second marriage was to a sister of Bird-Wilson.

11 WAAFs. Womens Auxiliary Air Force.

12 Pilots learned night approach and landings, and carried out simulated flying during the day, wearing goggles with specially coloured blue screens in the aircraft with sodium flares on the ground.

13 Bracknell, Berkshire.

14 Vertical Short Take Off and Landing.

15 Flight Sergeant.

16 RAF Shawbury.

17 A special 22,000 lb bomb used by 617 Squadron.

18 Marshal of the Royal Air Force.

19 AC2 – aircraftman second class.

20 401 Squadron.

ANSWERS RAF QUIZ 11

1   F1, F2, F3, Panavia, GR1.

2   Chief of Special Operations Executive, SOE (WW2) General Sir Colin Gubbins KCMG, DSO.

3   2 miles south of Telford.

4   Evaders.

5   James.

6   AWACs – Airborne Warning and Control Systems.

7   Ascension Island, 4000 miles away.

8   'Sparks'. They were radio operators if in aircrew or ground radio airmen or women.

9   Offensive op usually at night or in poor weather to a specified target or targets of opportunity.

10   RAF Rudloe Manor, Wiltshire.

11   71 Squadron.

12   4th SAS Regt (Chasseurs Parachutistes) a French force trained in guerilla warfare, dropped behind German lines from D-Day on.

13   Night intruders, as fighters or fighter bombers.

14   de Havilland.

15   Photographic Reconnaissance Unit.

16   Air Force Medal.

17   Spitfires and Hurricanes.

18 Proctors, Tiger Moths or Austers.

19 Walrus and Sea Otter.

20 The Mess.

ANSWERS RAF QUIZ 12

1 Observer.

2 Two.

3 University Air Squadrons.

4 A fighter pilot, more especially after he had made his first confirmed claim.

5 America.

6 German blind bombing system for bombers.

7 Non-flying RAF Officers.

8 A crash.

9 Anti-Aircraft guns or fire, or Ack Ack.

10 Chain Home Stations.

11 The adjutant.

12 Royal Norwegian Air Force.

13 601 RAuxAF. Royal Auxiliary Air Force Squadron.

14 605 RAuxAF Squadron.

15 193. A gift squadron, donated and named by the South American country, Brazil.

16 Rank of Group Captain and above.

17 Childs Ercall.

18 An open prison.

19 Non Commissioned Officer.

20 Sent to another station, unit or squadron.

ANSWERS RAF QUIZ 13

1 Hawker.

2 Three. Strike and Support Commands and RAF Germany.

3 Up to eight.

4 Sir Christopher Wren in 1682.

5 1957 – The infamous White Paper.

6 Squadrons financially donated by a country, city, group or similar and named for the donor – e.g. 247 (F) Squadron is called The China British through a subscription to the Air Ministry's Aeroplane Fund of 1940, by British and Allied residents in China.

7   It was the most famous mascot in the RAF, at 609 Squadron. There was a series of goats called 'Lewis' at the Apprentices School RAF Halton.

8   The best all-round unit.

9   Sand Pink.

10 'In Omnibus Princeps' – 'In All Things First'.

11 An airfield on Malta.

12 Brooklands in 1915.

13 Two.

14 10 Squadron. Each aircraft carried the name of a VC, including Guy Gibson, Albert Ball, James Nicholson, William Rhodes-Moorhouse.

15 A circus consisted of sweeps by light bombers accompanied by fighter escort in close and top cover. Intended to give enemy fighters a worthwhile target and to be dealt with by the Allied fighters.

16 Light sand colours with no squadron marking or roundels. Hemp colours for paint were adopted in the mid-1980s.

17 1990.

18 Singapore.

19 Transport Wing HQ, training on Hercules, and VIP treatment.

20 29 Squadron.

ANSWERS RAF QUIZ 14

1   Chichester – under the municipal liaison scheme of 1939.

2   British and allied residents in China contributed to the Aeroplane Fund for its formation.

3   The Chicken Farmers – looking after 43 the Fighting Cocks.

4   Two.

5   One.

6   A V1 Flying Bomb or Doodle Bug of 1944.

7   Surface to Air Missile.

8   Tornados.

9   In Borneo flying Javelins.

10   A Hawk. Flown by the Red Arrows.

11   25 years.

12   Baron Manfred von Richtofen.

13   Five.

14   So that the enemy could not identify a squadron or its home base.

15   One of sixteen Hunter aircraft of 111 squadron which in 1961 was the RAF's official aerobatic team.

16   SOE aircraft flying at night from Tangmere and Tempsford into enemy territory.

17   111 Squadron, or the Tremblers. The Black Arrow aerobatic team of 1957-60.

18 617, the Dambusters – a broken dam.

19 Centre front on a peaked hat or on the side of a side cap.

20 Civilian aircraft taken into RAF service.

ANSWERS RAF QUIZ 15

1 The Operation to recover the Falklands in 1982.

2 Aircraft hand general duties. Known as 'boggy', a person who did menial jobs including 'bog' cleaning.

3 Slang for a helicopter.

4 No 1 Group, No 11 Group, 18 Group, RAF Cyprus and RAF Hong Kong.

5 D-Day. The Allied invasion of Europe 6th June 1944.

6 Operation Plainfare.

7 Cumulo-Nimbus. It was potentially dangerous because pilots never knew how extensive it was.

8 Low level strikes into occupied Europe in poor weather by single-engined aircraft.

9 Any of the following: 58, 59, 120, 172, 179, 201, 206, 209, 224, 228, 407, 461, 269, 304, 311, 502, 612, 10 RAAF.

10 Navy, dark red and light blue.

11 A sweetheart brooch.

12 RAF Shawbury with Gazelle helicopters.

13 27.

14 Central Flying School – Scampton, Shawbury and Valley.

15 RAF Wyton.

16 617 Squadron, the Dambusters.

17 VC 10s.

18 A Typhoon with canon.

19 Part of the armoury of a Tornado F3. Medium range air-to-air guided missile.

20 Radar-guided medium-range sea-skimming missile carried by Nimrods in 1982.

ANSWERS RAF QUIZ 16

1 Sir David Craig; in 1991 CDS – Chief of Defence Staff – now Lord Craig.

2 Uxbridge, West Drayton or Northolt.

3 Cumbria, but in South Yorkshire in WW2 complaints were registered about the Dambusters practising over Ladybower reservoir. Events proved both wrong, low flying practice was essential and justified.

4 Germany.

5 Wing Commander Leonard Cheshire, later Group Capt VC. Died 1992.

6 9 January 1941.

7   Hereford.

8   The serial number shown is unique to each plane and the RAF Museum at Hendon holds the aircraft cards, which gives details of the plane's history.

9   RAF Greenham Common.

10 N.

11 RAF Swanton Morley.

12 The Joliffe Trophy.

13 Tom King.

14 In Air Sea Rescue. A Sea Otter was a rescue amphibian.

15 A Lieutenant Commander.

16 Name, rank and number.

17 A truce.

18 F for Freddie, S for Sugar, U for Uncle.

19 Roundel. The colours are red-white-blue.

20 Red and blue on wing top surface. Red, white and blue with yellow ring on fuselage. Dark blue and pale blue wings for SEAC aircraft.

ANSWERS RAF QUIZ 17

1 French. M'Aidez, help me.

2 Landing Ground; Advanced Landing Ground; In charge of; Other Ranks; Senior Air Staff Officer; Reserve of RAF Officers; With effect from; Rear gunner.

3 Left side.

4 In the air – a formation of aircraft facing the same way on the flank of and slightly to the rear of each other. On the ground – the service unit of a squadron, usually carrying its number preceded by 6.

5 The position or guide mark of an aircraft in flight for pilot or navigator to find bearings.

6 The line between stem and stern. Also airman's type of cap.

7 An unfixed number of Wings and their Support Units. The HQ of an area.

8 A. Marshal of the Royal Air Force. B. Air Chief Marshal. C. Air Marshal.

9 To move sideways in flight whilst going forward.

10 The Tigers.

11 Letchworth, Hertfordshire.

12 Wilkinson Sword Ltd.

13 Helicopters.

14 Wattisham and West Raynham.

15 Military Emergency Diversion Airfields.

16 RAF Lyneham, Wiltshire.

17   Take off vertically and land in the same way.

18   Led by Wing Commander Bird-Wilson DSO, DFC, later Air Vice Marshal.

19   Hercules.

20   On a Station Commander's Flag and also above the radiator on his vehicle. The three stars signify an Air Marshal.

ANSWERS RAF QUIZ 18

1   Was held at Greenham Common, then at RAF Fairford.

2   Cyprus.

3   The Distinguished Flying Cross and Bar.

4   3 July 1940 in 19 Squadron.

5   Supermarine Seafire.

6   Because two beer barrels had been unofficially fitted to the wing bomb racks. Typhoons also suffered the same 'fate'! Any other modification would have been given a number rather than XXX.

7   Letting the nose dip too low for take off and landing, bending the propeller.

8   In front of the RAF Church of St Clement Dane.

9   Faith Winter.

10   Gloster Meteor T7 VW453. Believed to be the oldest T7 in existence. Made in 1948 it carries the colours of 604 Squadron.

11 Cotswold Aircraft Restoration Group.

12 Flambards.

13 Hercules.

14 The School of Special Flying, Gosport.

15 A Wellington, R-Robert.

16 A V Roe – Avro.

17 B17F, a Flying Fortress.

18 An RAF aerobatic team based at Odiham.

19 RAF Scampton, Lincolnshire.

20 A cross on the lapel of his tunic or collar of his shirt.
His wartime badge had wings either side of the cross.

ANSWERS RAF QUIZ 19

1 Wg Cdr Don Kingaby.

2 The unsuccessful operation to assassinate Hitler in 1943 by a
bomb on board his aircraft.

3 The codename for the allied raid on Dieppe 19 August 1942.

4 1943. It was meant to draw up the Luftwaffe into battle,
making them believe the invasion was going to start in the
Pas de Calais.

5 The Anglo-American invasion of Casablanca, Algiers, and
Oran in French North Africa, 8 November 1942.

6   British Army of the Rhine. Yes, as 2nd TAF.

7   Antonov 124.

8   Spitfire Mk V (Va).

9   RAF Lyneham and Brize Norton.

10 Operation Granby.

11 P/O Eric Pentland, 17 June 1926 from an Avro 504.

12 Leslie Irvin on 19 April 1919 – founder of the Caterpillar Club.

13 Test pilot Ossie Lancaster in 1949.

14 Tony was in 43 at Tangmere and Pat was in 85.

15 Riyadh, Dhahran, and Tabuk.

16 1 Group at Upavon, 18 Group at Northwood, 11 Group at Bentley Priory.

17 20 Reserve Squadron, 42, 56, 16, 19, 60, 63 and 48 Squadron RAF Regt, and the Observer Corps.

18 It is a Folland Gnat and it was used by The Red Arrows before the Hawk.

19 RAF Marham.

20 Victor K2 tankers.

ANSWERS RAF QUIZ 20

1 The track running south of the Iraq border, the route into Iraq.

2 2 April 1982.

3 Wideawake.

4 1957.

5 It is a Harrier and it can take off vertically.

6 H E Bates who was in the RAFVR.

7 The duster.

8 The specialist press relations unit.

9 A two-seater fighter-bomber now specialising in Maritime attack. Served in Bahrain in 1991.

10 Messerschmitt 109.

11 About two minutes.

12 A flint arrowhead.

13 Since 1959.

14 Since 1976, and as navigators since 1977.

15 RAF Hendon in the 1920s.

16 Hector Bolitho, a Flight Lieutenant at HQ Coastal Command.

17 Sq Ldr Neville Duke.

18 The Parachute Regiment.

19 The plastic or fibre glass replicas which are used as gate guardians in place of the real thing now being taken into preservation.

20 Because both the Falklands and the Gulf Wars were combined services operations.

ANSWERS PHOTO QUIZ

A The SE5a. One Lewis machine gun on the top wing and one Vickers machine gun firing through the propeller.

B A Dornier Do17.

C General Adolf Galland.

D Wg Cdr John Cunningham, known as 'Cat's Eyes'.

E The Vickers Vimy.

F The Avro Shackleton.

G ACM Sir Hugh Dowding, C-in-C Fighter Command 1936-40.

H The Handley Page Halifax.

I The RE8. It was a reconnaissance plane.

BIBLIOGRAPHY

The Right of the Line. RAF in the European War 1939-45.
John Terraine.
Hodder and Stoughton 1985.

The Royal Air Force 1939-45 3 Vols.
Denis Richards and Hilary St George Saunders.
HMSO 1954.

Aircraft of the Royal Air Force since 1918.
Owen Thetford.
Putnam 1957-88.
(And the rest of the Putnam series on UK, USA and German
    aircraft types.)

Dictionary of Dates.
Audrey Butler. Everyman's Reference Library.
J M Dent 1987.

Men of the Battle of Britain.
Kenneth G Wynn.
Gliddon Books 1989.

Squadrons of the Royal Air Force and Commonwealth 1918-1988.
James J Halley.
Air Britain.

An Illustrated History of the RAF.
Roy Conyers Nesbit.
CLB 1990.

OTHER GRUB STREET AVIATION BOOKS

If you would like to go on our mailing list for details of these and forthcoming aviation publications, please send your name and address to:

GRUB STREET, THE BASEMENT, 10 CHIVALRY RD, LONDON SW11 1HT

TEST PILOT
Neville Duke DSO, OBE, DFC (Two Bars), AFC
Hardback   ISBN 0-948817-63-1   £16.95

TORPEDO LEADER
Wing Commander Patrick Gibbs, DSO DFC
Hardback   ISBN 0-948817-56-9   £16.95

OVER THE FRONT
Norman Franks and Frank Bailey
The Complete Record of The Fighter Aces and Units of the United States and French Air Services 1914-18
Hardback   ISBN 0-948817-54-2   £27.50

ABOVE THE TRENCHES
Christopher Shores, Norman Franks and Russell Guest
The Complete Record of The Fighter Aces of the British Empire Air Forces 1915-1920
Hardback   ISBN 0-948817-19-4   £35.00

BLOODY SHAMBLES
Christopher Shores, Brian Cull and Yasuho Izawa
The First Comprehensive Account of Air Operations over South-East Asia, December 1941–April 1942. Volume One – The Drift to War to the Fall of Singapore
Hardback   ISBN 0-948817-50-X   £27.50

FLEDGLING EAGLES
Christopher Shores and Others
The Complete Account of Air War over Western Europe and Scandinavia, September 1939–August 1940
Hardback   ISBN 0-948817-42-9   £27.50

MALTA: The Hurricane Years 1940-41
Christopher Shores and Brian Cull with Nicola Malizia
Hardback   ISBN 0-948817-06-2   £20.00

MALTA: The Spitfire Year 1942
Christopher Shores and Brian Cull with Nicola Malizia
Hardback   ISBN 0-948817-16-X   £32.50

AIR WAR FOR YUGOSLAVIA, GREECE AND CRETE 1940-41
Christopher Shores and Brian Cull with Nicola Malizia
Hardback   ISBN 0-948817-07-0   £20.00

FOR VALOUR: THE AIR VC'S
Chaz Bowyer
Hardback   ISBN 0-948817-57-7   £29.95

THE GREATEST AIR BATTLE
Norman Franks
Dieppe, 19th August 1942 – 50th Anniversary Edition
Hardback   ISBN 0-948817-58-5   £17.95